Dad and Sam

Written by Leslie McGuire   Illustrated by Mitchell Rose

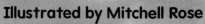

Hooked On Phonics®

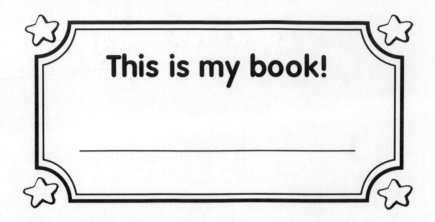

This is my book!

_____

While HOP Companion Books can be used independently, this series of books has been designed as a supplement to Level 1 of the *Hooked on Phonics*® • *Learn to Read* program.

When to read: Read after HOP Book 2, *Rag*.

Phonics practice: Words with short **a** sound, such as *Dad* and *hat*

Dad and Sam

Written by Leslie McGuire • Illustrated by Mitchell Rose

Hooked On Phonics®

ISBN 1-887942-67-X

Dad had a hat.

Dad had a nap.

Sam had the hat.

Sam ran and ran.
WAP!

Can Dad nap?

Dad can pat Sam.

Sam can nap on Dad.